Bonjour

1ère Partie, Unité 1

Barbara Scanes

3

5

7

Vocabulaire

bonjour	good morning/hello
écoutez	listen
levez-vous	get up
regardez	look
un crocodile	a crocodile
non	no
c'est moi	it's me
maman	mum
alors	so
s'il vous plaît	please

Luc et Sophie – a challenge

Colour in the picture and write what you think maman is saying in the speech bubble. (This page may be photocopied.)

Bonjour

Barbara Scanes

Maman tries to wake up Luc and Sophie. She calls out 'Bonjour Luc ! Bonjour Sophie ! Levez-vous !' The children stay fast asleep. What can she do to make them wake up?

Bonjour is one of the stories in *Learn French with Luc et Sophie*, a story-based scheme for teaching French in primary schools.

Full details of the scheme can be found on: www.brilliantpublications.co.uk

ISBN-13: 978-1-78317-148-4

Brilliant
PUBLICATIONS